Award Winning Trilogy Collection

AWARD WINNING TRILOGY COLLECTION

BELIEVE

Best Selling Books by Artist N.A. Noël

INCLUDING

Believe

On Earth As It Is In Heaven

All God's Creatures Go To Heaven

Some of the original paintings in this book are available as fine art prints. For information on purchasing prints, award winning books or to request a free Noël Studio color catalog:

Noël Studio, Inc.
75 North Main Street
Zionsville, Indiana 46077
1-800-444-6635
www.nanoel.com

"The Believe Trilogy"

Original cover designs by Betsy Knotts · Trilogy cover design by Jennifer Bradley-Simmons

ISBN: 1-59795-398-9

BELIEVE

Original Paintings by N.A. Noël
Original Poetry by John Wm. Sisson

Do you believe?
Then tell me...

Have you heard an angel pray,
Perhaps for love and grace?
What would an angel have to say
In such a heavenly place?

What words of joy and those of praise
Would angels give a voice?
When speaking of warm summer days,
What words would be their choice?

And flowers in the early spring
On hill or forest lawn,
What would a heavenly angel sing
To greet them every dawn?

Or maybe on a mountain top
Or in a valley wide,
Or any place that makes you stop
Where angels play and hide.

One wonders of the words they'd use,
What songs would they inspire?
Which poems would the angels choose
From an angel heart's desire?

Wisdom

Wisdom is an angel friend you'll find
When you explore,
Through knowledge and experience
What lies behind life's door.

Wisdom leads you from the darkness
Moving toward the light,
By teaching you to find the wrong
And turn it into right.

Wisdom moves with generations
Father to the Son,
A cycle of renewal
Making Mother, Daughter one.

With Wisdom comes enlightenment
Of who we really are,
Living beings on a planet
Circling 'round a star.

Wisdom with her nature's crown
Will light upon your being,
The flowering of her glory
So much more than we are seeing.

For each of us to everyone just like
A simple flower,
Becomes a living sample of the
Beauty of God's power.

Wisdom's universal song for
Humankind is true,
You must do unto others what you
Wish done unto you.

Peace & Harmony

Here are two that are so close
They always stay in tune;
How could we have the shining sun
Without the silvery moon?

The only way that you'll find Peace
Is finding Harmony,
And when you find the two of them
They both will set you free.

Just sit there still with Harmony
And close your eyes with Peace,
And soon you'll feel an inner strength
From a source that will not cease.

It's when there's Peace and Harmony
That all of us can grow;
Beyond those of our wildest dreams,
Beyond yet what we know.

Side by side and on through time
Go Peace and Harmony,
And trust me when you find the one
There will the other be.

Faith

Here we are with little Faith
A giant without measure,
It's those who keep a little Faith
Who always find life's treasure.

A little Faith will guide us on
Through darkest hour of night,
While others may not see the dawn
We'll see her morning light.

Who knows, with just a little Faith
And all her angel's charm
We'll make our mother planet safe,
All creatures safe from harm.

From flowers in the fertile fields
To mountains fresh with snow,
Abundance from God's bounty yields
The fruits that make Faith grow.

So you can see with love and grace
And even joy unbound,
It's good to keep about the place
A little Faith around.

Humility

Everyday with Humility
We always make our way,
She gives us the ability
To humble what we say.

We always seek her tender eyes
When cast in our direction,
We're humbled as we realize
The depth of her affection.

Humility sits there with grace
She waits upon the faithful,
And humbly she sets a place
For even those ungrateful.

Humility with charity
An honored way to give,
A gift from your sincerity
That helps another live.

Humility in all we do
Though through this life we stumble,
In every age they always knew
That God rewards the humble.

Love

Of all the angels high above
There's one above the rest.
Of course this angel's name is Love
Among us all most blest.

Love's in the air caressing spring
With every passing breeze.
Love's in the warmth that summer brings,
Love's in the autumn leaves.

Love's in the souls that are so pure
Who seek for God's salvation;
He helps their spirits to endure
Through faith and adoration.

Love's in the causes won and lost
For Love is in the labor.
We all forget the trials crossed
When seeking Love's sweet favor.

Love guides our angel's every move
Which isn't all that odd.
How could we work or scarce improve
Without the Love of God?

Charity

There's one who speaks with clarity
And gentleness of mind.
We love our friend sweet Charity
For acts she does divine.

Yes, Charity can feed the poor;
She helps the sick and tired.
Those brought low before her door
Leave fresh, renewed, inspired.

An act to lend a helping hand
To a stranger or a neighbor,
Will resonate throughout the land
And always win God's favor.

That's the part in all our minds
That seems the most sincere,
The joy of giving each one finds
With Charity each year.

Hope

It's Hope that's there when you're in need
To somewhere, somehow plant the seed
That yes, there's Hope to carry on;
Support the weak and make them strong.

Whatever contest may be held
Or when it seems your cause be felled,
When all seems lost and without reason
Hope springs alive; she'll have her season.

That little seed from long ago
She planted there will start to grow,
Because of Hope we'll all survive
Because we all kept Hope alive.

That seed she nestled in our breast
That helps make us our very best,
An angel's gift she loves to share
You'll always know that Hope is there.

Miracle

Do you believe in Miracles?
Well all the angels do,
If you knew our friend Miracle
Then you'd believe them too.

The miracles that she performs
Delight us through the ages,
From magic to the unicorns
To wisdom from the sages.

The Miracle of faith is one,
Friendship is another,
The Golden Rule, the golden sun,
A baby with its Mother.

Why Miracles are everywhere,
They're in a child's eyes,
A tree, a leaf beyond compare,
The colors in the skies.

The Miracle of planet earth
We're told by all our teachers,
Is way beyond a scale of worth
When weighing all God's creatures.

The greatest gift they say of all
Through laughter, joy and strife,
All God's angels simply call,
The Miracle of life.

Grace

Here's the one with such a face
That all of us will seek for Grace,
So full of charm with virtue mild
This gift to us this graceful child.

You always know when Grace takes wing,
The sun will shine, the birds will sing;
And everywhere in every place
The world will seem so full of Grace.

By Grace of God we use our time
To contemplate these things divine;
And when we take our slumber here,
We have no doubt or even fear
That Grace of God will guide us on,
Protect our night from dusk to dawn,
And every morn her wish will be,
We'll rise anew so gracefully.

And when the day is nearly done,
With each success that you have won,
It's then God's angels sing with glee,
We're glad to grant our Grace to thee.

 Compassion

Compassion is an angel
Who always gives her all,
She's there for every creature
Whether great or whether small.

At any time of day or night
Or any kind of storm,
She'll wrap her arms around your soul
To keep you safe and warm.

Compassion swells within a heart
When someone is in pain,
It softly beats a rhythm
So gentle and humane.

No matter if it's man or beast
Or what their tale of woe,
Compassion with her wings outstretched
Will help the healing grow.

Compassion has a kindness
Seen in every tender act.
So when you're kind to someone else
I tell you it's a fact…
Sometime she'll be around again
For all the angels say,
Compassion shown to others
Will be shown to you someday.

To my sons, Alexander and Michael...
who taught me to **Believe***.*

– N.A. NOËL

To my Grandmother, my Mother, my Sister
and Nancy Noël for their encouragement, love and
dedication to God.

– JOHN WM. SISSON

Our prayer for you

Angels are a gift to us,
They come from God above.
You'll feel them all about you,
When you live your life with love.

As the seasons take their turn
We hope with joy and care,
It is our wish you'll feel the bliss
Of all the angels there.

We hope you find the magic
And the wisdom of the wise,
Who knew that everything they saw
Could not be seen with eyes.

So with a humble spirit
We hope that this will fill,
A spot deep within your heart
With solitude so still.

You'll know that this angelic art
And this poetic rhyme
Is made for you and yes it's true,
For you throughout all time.

Please let this be our prayer for you
That every single day,
You feel angels everywhere
In all you do and say.

No matter whether clouds are gray
Or skies of crystal blue,
You'll always know that with our love
We send this book to you...

John

Your truth is God's truth
and always your surest answer —
as awesome as the night sky,
as simple as a child's smile,
as loud as a pounding heartbeat,
and as quiet as a breath taken
in unity with Him.

— "Conversations with God"
as brought through by
Neale Donald Walsch

On Earth as it is in Heaven

Paintings by N.A. Noël
Story by N.A. Noël and John Wm. Sisson

My soul can find no staircase to Heaven
unless it be through the Earth's loveliness.

– *Michelangelo*

This book is dedicated to
Georgia, who loved me, and
to all my friends and family.
It is on the wind from your wings that I fly...
and it is your light that guides me.

— *N. A. Noël*

With love and affection
to my brother Fred, who has been
my guardian angel all my life.

— *John Wm. Sisson*

Rosie stood there in Heaven and stretched out her wings,
so soft and so white, such marvelous things!

Now she could flip as she flew in the air —
maybe fly to the stars…why, fly anywhere!

Just as she thought this, an angel appeared.
"Oh my," said the angel, "it's just as I feared.

"Those wings that we gave you may be a bit wide.
We could pluck them or tuck them or trim up the side."

"Forgive me," said Rosie, "I don't know your name.
Please, may I keep them the way that they came?

"I like all this white and I like all this fluff.
I like all the things I can do with this stuff."

"Wisdom is my name. I'll be your good friend.
When little ones come here, I'm the angel they send.

"I'm glad that you're happy with Heaven's new gift.
They're wings for your spirit, to give you a lift!

"It always takes wisdom to see your way through,
especially up here, where all things seem new."

"You're right!" giggled Rosie. "Why, look over there! Those crystals are gleaming and floating in air!"

"Rosie," said Wisdom, "remember the mirth
and laughter and fun when it snowed back on Earth?

"Those gentle flakes, like a lamb in the snow,
are glimpses of Heaven and the beauty we know.

"Like these flowers I'm wearing, entwined in my crown,
are proof to us all that God is around.

"Think back to the summer, when you walked by the sea,
with the waves full of sunlight…that sunlight was me!

"Like the seagull who waits for the wind to take flight,
we all have to choose what's wrong or what's right.

"You need to look and learn to take time
to see all God's beauty and, especially, be kind.

"These things are so easy, when you know God is here.
He's always beside you and within you, my dear.

"You are His child and always have been,
and so are your friends, both Rachel and Ben.

"Remember last fall with the leaves on the ground?
Remember the fawn the three of you found?

"You wondered at nature and how she revealed
the mystery and magic of what she concealed.

"This light of God's wisdom is something we share —
on Earth, as in Heaven…why, it's everywhere!"

"Oh please, precious Wisdom, may I go back to Earth,
to show Ben and Rachel what life's really worth?

"Rachel is two
and Ben is only three.
I know they may wonder,
when they think about me.

"How can I tell them I want them to know
that God's all around them, just like the young doe
whose sweetness is hidden as she lies in the leaves,
but is easily found by someone's good deeds?

"I'll touch their hearts, when a cloud passes by,
and whenever it's dark, I'll be their star in the sky.

"When flowers are blooming, I'll let them know
that Heaven is found in the roses that grow.

"I'll open their eyes to all they can see
and be to each other the best they can be."

"In a second you'll be there, and so will the dawn.
You can show them the seagull, the lamb, and the fawn.

"Go tell the children to tell all their friends
that love is forever and love never ends.

"Awaken the knowledge that shows them the worth
of knowing that Heaven can be here on Earth!"

Rosie looked toward the stars as she fluffed up her wings.
"I'll go back as an angel and show them these things."

"God will be pleased," said Wisdom, "by the good that you do,
which brings out the spirit of the love within you.

"He must have known, when He ordered your wings,
the size of your love and the gifts that it brings.

"Now soar as an angel through God's starry night,
and bring to your friends His wisdom and light."

This story is in memory of Therrian.

Fly

Fly, fly little wing
Fly beyond imagining
The softest cloud the whitest dove
Upon the wind of Heaven's love
Past the planets and the stars
Leave this lonely world of ours
Escape the sorrow and the pain
And fly again

Fly, fly precious one
Your endless journey has begun
Take your gentle happiness
Far too beautiful for this
Cross over to the other shore
There is peace forevermore
But hold this mem'ry bittersweet
Until we meet

Fly, fly do not fear
Don't waste a breath don't shed a tear
Your heart is pure, your soul is free
Be on your way don't wait for me
Above the universe you'll climb
On beyond the hands of time
The moon will rise the sun will set
But I won't forget

Fly, fly little wing
Fly where only angels sing
Fly away, the time is right
Go now, find the light

Jean-Jaques Goldman & Phil Gladston

All God's Creatures Go To Heaven

ORIGINAL PAINTINGS BY N.A. NOËL

An Original Short Story By Amy Nolfo-Wheeler

To my Uncle Bobby who shared my love for animals,
and my horse El Kadere who filled my life with devotion.

N.A Noël

To my Mother & Father for their love and belief in me,
and to Buster, my childhood dog and dear old friend; whose memory inspired this story.

A.A. Nolfo-Wheeler

In Heaven, children angels spend their days frolicking in ever blossoming gardens filled with brightly colored flowers. They play among sweet scented fruit trees on soft wind-swept grassy pathways.

In Heaven, children angels sometimes nap in the warmth of the sunlight and other times dance barefoot and spread their wings to enjoy the tickle of an occasional shower. There are no thunderstorms in Heaven, just gentle rains that are always followed by

ainbows.

Jacob is a little boy who lives in Heaven with lots of other children angels from all over the world. Jacob loves Heaven and he loves being an angel. In Heaven he was reunited with his Grandmother and Grandfather. Though only six years old he could remember his Grandmother's gentle touch and the fun he and his Grandfather had playing in his big backyard on Earth. In Heaven there is no pain or sorrow. Jacob does not feel sad that his parents are not with him; instead he rejoices that one day they will all be together again forever and ever.

Weeks passed and Jacob began to notice that his angel friends were caring for all kinds of different creatures. Some children had dogs while others had cats or bunnies or goats.

One shy, sweet, little angel, Micheal had a gentle, fuzzy llama named Minnie.

Jacob wanted a pet to care for too. On Earth he had a white puppy he called Gracie and a mouse by the name of Morsel. Morsel's favorite pastime was sitting in the palm of Jacob's hand while nibbling a piece of cheese. Gracie and Jacob would play in the park for hours and then come home to rest in the shade of Jacob's favorite tree.

One afternoon Jacob asked Angelica, a wise child angel, where the creatures in Heaven came from. Jacob admired Angelica's beautiful white dove. Angelica was delighted by Jacob's inquiry and decided he was ready to learn about his special purpose in Heaven.

"You see Jacob," whispered Angelica, "children have an important and wonderful purpose here. These extraordinary creatures that are being cared for by the children of Heaven all once had a life on Earth, just like you."

"You mean like my puppy Gracie on Earth?"

"Yes, Jacob, just like Gracie."

"Here we entrust the children angels with the care of these loyal animals. This is because little children and all of these loving pets have very similar souls. Children and their pets have a lot in common."

"I don't understand" said Jacob with a shrug, "I don't remember being anything like my puppy Gracie."

"Well you certainly didn't have a furry coat or a wagging tail," chuckled Angelica, "but your hearts were in the same place. Children and animals are both innocent; they need our gentle care, respect and love. Children and animals are two of God's greatest gifts to the world; their love is honest and true. Animals are a blessing Jacob, just like you."

"But why do the other children have animal companions and I do not?"

"Well, you were new here Jacob. Caring for an animal is a big responsibility; I felt you should take some time to get to know your new surroundings before your first assignment."

"Assignment? What assignment?"

"Your special purpose, Jacob ~ and the special purpose of all little children in Heaven is being trusted with the care of a pet. Some angels are assigned to ponies while others care for kittens, birds or even lambs!

We know that children can give animals loving attention until they are reunited with their human companions. At that time, you will receive a new animal to love. You are going to have many beautiful and enchanting animal friends here in Heaven Jacob!"

"Oh Angelica, I can't wait any longer for my assignment... may I have one soon?" Jacob's wings fluttered with anticipation.

"As a matter of fact, a friend arrived for you today, a heavenly friend whose name is Snowflake!" In an instant there was a burst of Stardust and suddenly a big fluffy bunny rabbit appeared in Jacob's arms. Jacob embraced his new friend with all the love his heart could give. He quickly gave Snowflake a kiss on the head. Jacob felt warm and happy; there were no words to express his joy. He turned toward the gardens, excited to share the arrival of his new friend with the other angels.

Just before Jacob flew away he turned back toward Angelica...

"Angelica?" He said softly, "this means that not just people go to Heaven?"

"Yes Jacob, it means all God's creatures go to Heaven."

"Even Gracie?" Jacob asked with a smile.

"Yes, Jacob, someday even Gracie."

he nd

In memory of our white rabbit, *Fluff 'n Stuff*.